C000147225

Spelling is part of Primary English _whether they like it or not_

'Spelling Superstar or Spelling Swamp Dweller' works by setting clear targets. We think kids do better if they know exactly what they're being asked to do...

> ## AT LEAST 50% OF SPELLINGS MUST BE CORRECT
> ## BY THE END OF THE YEAR

...and this book gives kids lots of practice to make sure they do.

Here's how it works...

1) *Make sure the whole class knows that:*
   - *the point of this book is to BE A SPELLING SUPERSTAR*
   - *you stay a Superstar by meeting targets*
   - *to do well in primary English you must get at least 50% of spellings right*

2) *We've left a space for you to write a target at the top of each page, e.g. 5/20 or 25%.*

3) *Targets should get tougher over the year.*

4) *If a child meets their target, they're a Superstar, but if they miss one they become a Swamp Dweller — until next time they meet their targets.*

5) *Then you can circle the Superstar or Swamp Dweller at the top of each page.*

6) *Even better, make a massive poster, with stickers for the kids' names. Move the names from Superstar to Swamp Dweller in a weekly ceremony. Give prizes for becoming a Superstar, and punishments for becoming a Swamp Dweller — may we suggest running round the school waving their hands in the air shouting, "I've got smelly pants and I don't care!" or doing the page again for homework.*

Double letters

Copy out the words once, cover with the flap and write them again.
Get _____ right to become a Spelling Superstar.

Read	Copy	Cover
1) dinner	1	1
2) tapping	2	2
3) hopping	3	3
4) pollen	4	4
5) hippo	5	5
6) grabbed	6	6
7) written	7	7
8) tennis	8	8
9) jolly	9	9
10) running	10	10
11) shopping	11	11
12) swimming	12	12
13) kettle	13	13
14) swallow	14	14
15) butter	15	15
16) carry	16	16
17) summer	17	17
18) pepper	18	18
19) willow	19	19
20) carrot	20	20

EXTRA PRACTICE		
E1) coffee	E1	E1
E2) common	E2	E2

Double letters

Put the flap over the last page and use the hints to work out the words.
Get _____ right to become a Spelling Superstar.

Hint hint	One last time...
1) Evening meal.	1 ....
2) Knocking gently.	2 ....
3) Bouncing up and down on one leg.	3 ....
4) Dusty stuff in flowers.	4 ....
5) One of these:	5 ....
6) Took hold of.	6 ....
7) Put down on paper, in words.	7 ....
8) A ball game.	8 ....
9) Cheerful.	9 ....
10) Moving with quick steps.	10 ....
11) Buying things.	11 ....
12) Moving through water.	12 ....
13) Boil water in this.	13 ....
14) Bird that flies south for the winter.	14 ....
15) Spread this on your toast.	15 ....
16) Hold in your hands.	16 ....
17) The hottest season.	17 ....
18) Hot seasoning.	18 ....
19) Type of tree — weeping _ _ _ _ _ _.	19 ....
20) Orange vegetable.	20 ....

EXTRA PRACTICE

E1) Hot drink.	E1 ....
E2) Not rare.	E2 ....

Word roots

Copy out the words once, cover with the flap and write them again.
Get _____ right to become a Spelling Superstar.

Read	Copy	Cover
1) express	1	1
2) pressure	2	2
3) aquarium	3	3
4) aqueduct	4	4
5) microlight	5	5
6) microscope	6	6
7) octagon	7	7
8) octopus	8	8
9) copy	9	9
10) photocopy	10	10
11) royal	11	11
12) royalty	12	12
13) manual	13	13
14) manuscript	14	14
15) spectator	15	15
16) spectrum	16	16
17) voice	17	17
18) vocal	18	18
19) blockage	19	19
20) blockade	20	20

EXTRA PRACTICE		
E1) announce	E1	E1
E2) noun	E2	E2

Word roots

Put the flap over the last page and use the hints to work out the words.
Get _____ right to become a Spelling Superstar.

Hint hint

One last time...

1) Say what you think or mean.

1 ....

2) Strain, stress, demands.

2 ....

3) Tank to keep fish in.

3 ....

4) A bridge that carries water.

4 ....

5) Very small, light aircraft.

5 ....

6) Makes things look much bigger.

6 ....

7) Eight-sided shape.

7 ....

8) Eight-legged animal.

8 ....

9) Repeat.

9 ....

10) Make a copy on a machine.

10 ....

11) Of kings and queens.

11 ....

12) Kings, queens, princes...

12 ....

13) By hand.

13 ....

14) A handwritten book.

14 ....

15) Someone watching an event.

15 ....

16) A rainbow.

16 ....

17) Sound made in a human throat.

17 ....

18) Spoken or sung.

18 ....

19) Something in the way.

19 ....

20) Surrounds or blocks something.

20 ....

EXTRA PRACTICE

E1) Make known to the public.

E1 ....

E2) Naming word.

E2 ....

v and k words

Copy out the words once, cover with the flap and write them again.
Get _____ right to become a Spelling Superstar.

Read	Copy	Cover
1) vase	1	1
2) valley	2	2
3) village	3	3
4) visit	4	4
5) novel	5	5
6) river	6	6
7) favour	7	7
8) invent	8	8
9) kick	9	9
10) kerb	10	10
11) broken	11	11
12) kitten	12	12
13) king	13	13
14) wrinkle	14	14
15) stoked	15	15
16) ankle	16	16
17) back	17	17
18) walk	18	18
19) dock	19	19
20) wink	20	20

EXTRA PRACTICE		
E1) prevent	E1	E1
E2) chuckle	E2	E2

v and k words

Put the flap over the last page and use the hints to work out the words.
Get _____ right to become a Spelling Superstar.

Hint hint	One last time...
1) For putting flowers in.	1 ....
2) Gap between two hills.	2 ....
3) Small town.	3 ....
4) Go to see.	4 ....
5) Fiction book.	5 ....
6) Flowing water — a big stream.	6 ....
7) Act of kindness.	7 ....
8) Make up.	8 ....
9) Hit with your foot.	9 ....
10) Edge of the pavement.	10 ....
11) Not working any more.	11 ....
12) Young cat.	12 ....
13) Ruler of a country.	13 ....
14) Small crease in the skin.	14 ....
15) Fed and looked after a fire.	15 ....
16) Joint between leg and foot.	16 ....
17) Not front.	17 ....
18) Move on your legs.	18 ....
19) Where ships are moored.	19 ....
20) Close one eye.	20 ....

EXTRA PRACTICE

E1) Stop something happening.	E1 ....
E2) Laugh.	E2 ....

wa, wo, ss

Copy out the words once, cover with the flap and write them again.
Get _____ right to become a Spelling Superstar.

Read	Copy	Cover
1) wasp	1	1
2) wander	2	2
3) warn	3	3
4) wave	4	4
5) swamp	5	5
6) swarm	6	6
7) dwarf	7	7
8) wolf	8	8
9) wonder	9	9
10) word	10	10
11) woman	11	11
12) sword	12	12
13) awoke	13	13
14) two	14	14
15) massive	15	15
16) missile	16	16
17) possession	17	17
18) guess	18	18
19) goodness	19	19
20) likeness	20	20

EXTRA PRACTICE		
E1) wallet	E1	E1
E2) possible	E2	E2

wa, wo, ss

Put the flap over the last page and use the hints to work out the words.
Get _____ right to become a Spelling Superstar.

Hint hint	One last time...
1) Insect with a sting.	1 ....
2) Walk around.	2 ....
3) Tell people about a danger.	3 ....
4) Hold up your hand in greeting.	4 ....
5) Boggy place.	5 ....
6) Big group of insects.	6 ....
7) Short person.	7 ....
8) Wild dog.	8 ....
9) Think about something.	9 ....
10) Take my _ _ _ _ for it.	10 ....
11) Female person.	11 ....
12) Long knife.	12 ....
13) Stopped sleeping.	13 ....
14) More than one but less than three.	14 ....
15) Big and heavy.	15 ....
16) Flying weapon.	16 ....
17) Something that's yours.	17 ....
18) Say what you think is most likely.	18 ....
19) Kindness, virtue.	19 ....
20) A picture of someone.	20 ....

EXTRA PRACTICE

E1) Flat case for holding money.	E1 ....
E2) Able to be done.	E2 ....

ad, af, al, a

Copy out the words once, cover with the flap and write them again.
Get _____ right to become a Spelling Superstar.

Read	Copy	Cover
1) adjective	1	1
2) advise	2	2
3) advance	3	3
4) addition	4	4
5) adjacent	5	5
6) affix	6	6
7) affluent	7	7
8) afflict	8	8
9) affect	9	9
10) afloat	10	10
11) almighty	11	11
12) already	12	12
13) always	13	13
14) altogether	14	14
15) almost	15	15
16) aloft	16	16
17) aloud	17	17
18) asleep	18	18
19) ablaze	19	19
20) around	20	20

EXTRA PRACTICE		
E1) alert	E1	E1
E2) affable	E2	E2

ad, af, al, a

Put the flap over the last page and use the hints to work out the words.
Get _____ right to become a Spelling Superstar.

Hint hint	One last time...
1) Describing word.	1 ....
2) Recommend something.	2 ....
3) Go forward.	3 ....
4) Adding numbers together. 2+2=	4 ....
5) Next to.	5 ....
6) Attach.	6 ....
7) Well off.	7 ....
8) Cause suffering.	8 ....
9) To produce an effect on something.	9 ....
10) Held up by water or air.	10 ....
11) All-powerful.	11 ....
12) Before this time.	12 ....
13) Forever.	13 ....
14) Totally, completely.	14 ....
15) Nearly.	15 ....
16) Up in the air.	16 ....
17) Audible, not silent.	17 ....
18) Not awake.	18 ....
19) On fire.	19 ....
20) On every side.	20 ....

EXTRA PRACTICE

E1) Watchful, ready.	E1 ....
E2) Friendly.	E2 ....

s, ed, ing

Copy out the words once, cover with the flap and write them again.
Get _____ right to become a Spelling Superstar.

Read	Copy	Cover
1) shows	1	1
2) showed	2	2
3) showing	3	3
4) works	4	4
5) worked	5	5
6) working	6	6
7) cries	7	7
8) cried	8	8
9) crying	9	9
10) hugs	10	10
11) hugged	11	11
12) hugging	12	12
13) explores	13	13
14) explored	14	14
15) exploring	15	15
16) fizzes	16	16
17) fizzed	17	17
18) fizzing	18	18
19) hisses	19	19
20) hissing	20	20

EXTRA PRACTICE		
E1) buzzes	E1	E1
E2) buzzed	E2	E2

s, ed, ing

Put the flap over the last page and use the hints to work out the words.
Get _____ right to become a Spelling Superstar.

Hint hint	One last time...
1) Another word for demonstrates.	1 ....
2) Demonstrated.	2 ....
3) Demonstrating.	3 ....
4) Another word for studies.	4 ....
5) Studied.	5 ....
6) Studying.	6 ....
7) Another word for 'sheds tears'.	7 ....
8) Shed tears.	8 ....
9) Shedding tears.	9 ....
10) Another word for cuddles.	10 ....
11) Cuddled.	11 ....
12) Cuddling.	12 ....
13) Another word for investigates.	13 ....
14) Investigated.	14 ....
15) Investigating.	15 ....
16) Another word for bubbles.	16 ....
17) Bubbled.	17 ....
18) Bubbling.	18 ....
19) What a snake does when it's angry.	19 ....
20) Present tense of number 19).	20 ....

EXTRA PRACTICE

E1) What a bee does (a noise).	E1 ....
E2) What a bee did.	E2 ....

Spelling Book 2 — Word Endings

al, ary, ic

Copy out the words once, cover with the flap and write them again.
Get _____ right to become a Spelling Superstar.

Read	Copy	Cover
1) medical	1	1
2) personal	2	2
3) exceptional	3	3
4) national	4	4
5) sensational	5	5
6) additional	6	6
7) capital	7	7
8) stationary	8	8
9) revolutionary	9	9
10) missionary	10	10
11) necessary	11	11
12) library	12	12
13) salary	13	13
14) dictionary	14	14
15) historic	15	15
16) supersonic	16	16
17) traffic	17	17
18) horrific	18	18
19) angelic	19	19
20) epidemic	20	20

EXTRA PRACTICE		
E1) February	E1	E1
E2) rhythmic	E2	E2

al, ary, ic

Put the flap over the last page and use the hints to work out the words.
Get _____ right to become a Spelling Superstar.

Hint hint	One last time...
1) To do with medicine.	1
2) Nobody else's business.	2
3) Really good at something.	3
4) Country-wide.	4
5) Absolutely fantastic.	5
6) One more thing to add.	6
7) Letter for starting sentences with.	7
8) Not moving at all.	8
9) Groundbreaking.	9
10) Religious man who teaches people.	10
11) It has to happen.	11
12) Where you borrow books from.	12
13) Another word for wages.	13
14) Look words up in this book.	14
15) Event in the history books.	15
16) Faster than the speed of sound.	16
17) Cars in a jam.	17
18) Absolutely horrible.	18
19) Acting like an angel.	19
20) Large outbreak of disease.	20

EXTRA PRACTICE

E1) The second month.	E1
E2) Able to dance in time.	E2

ship, hood

Copy out the words once, cover with the flap and write them again.
Get _____ right to become a Spelling Superstar.

Read	Copy	Cover
1) membership	1	1
2) partnership	2	2
3) craftsmanship	3	3
4) fellowship	4	4
5) championship	5	5
6) dictatorship	6	6
7) ownership	7	7
8) workmanship	8	8
9) apprenticeship	9	9
10) friendship	10	10
11) childhood	11	11
12) falsehood	12	12
13) priesthood	13	13
14) neighbourhood	14	14
15) fatherhood	15	15
16) motherhood	16	16
17) knighthood	17	17
18) sisterhood	18	18
19) brotherhood	19	19
20) adulthood	20	20

EXTRA PRACTICE		
E1) marksmanship	E1	E1
E2) orphanhood	E2	E2

ship, hood

Put the flap over the last page and use the hints to work out the words.
Get _____ right to become a Spelling Superstar.

Hint hint	One last time...
1) Being a member of something.	1
2) Being partners.	2
3) Being good at making things.	3
4) There's one in Lord of the Rings.	4
5) Type of tournament.	5
6) Where one person rules a country.	6
7) Owning something.	7
8) Good solid work.	8
9) Being an apprentice.	9
10) Two friends are in one.	10
11) Being a kid.	11
12) Another word for a lie.	12
13) A group of priests.	13
14) You and your neighbours live in it.	14
15) Being a father.	15
16) Being a mother.	16
17) People call you 'sir' if you get one.	17
18) Group of women such as nuns.	18
19) Group of men such as monks.	19
20) Being an adult.	20

EXTRA PRACTICE

E1) Being a good shot.	E1
E2) Being an orphan.	E2

© CGP 2002

Spelling Book 2 — Word Endings

ness, ment

Copy out the words once, cover with the flap and write them again.
Get _____ right to become a Spelling Superstar.

Read	Copy	Cover
1) fairness	1	1
2) tidiness	2	2
3) nastiness	3	3
4) carelessness	4	4
5) loveliness	5	5
6) foolishness	6	6
7) willingness	7	7
8) silliness	8	8
9) fitness	9	9
10) forgetfulness	10	10
11) enjoyment	11	11
12) employment	12	12
13) ornament	13	13
14) movement	14	14
15) ointment	15	15
16) replacement	16	16
17) statement	17	17
18) document	18	18
19) environment	19	19
20) government	20	20

EXTRA PRACTICE		
E1) worthlessness	E1	E1
E2) management	E2	E2

ness, ment

Put the flap over the last page and use the hints to work out the words.
Get _____ right to become a Spelling Superstar.

Hint hint	One last time...
1) Being fair.	1
2) Being tidy.	2
3) Being nasty.	3
4) Being careless.	4
5) Being lovely.	5
6) Being foolish.	6
7) Being willing to do something.	7
8) Being silly.	8
9) Being fit and healthy.	9
10) Being absent-minded.	10
11) Fun to be had.	11
12) Having a job.	12
13) A vase or clock or porcelain doll.	13
14) Moving around.	14
15) Rub on your skin if you have a rash.	15
16) Something to replace a broken one.	16
17) Make a short prepared speech.	17
18) A piece of paper with work on it.	18
19) Look after it or the icecaps will melt.	19
20) People who run a country.	20

EXTRA PRACTICE

E1) Having no value at all.	E1
E2) The bosses.	E2

ate, en, ify, ise, ity

Copy out the words once, cover with the flap and write them again.
Get _____ right to become a Spelling Superstar.

Read	Copy	Cover
1) pollinate	1	1
2) medicate	2	2
3) elasticate	3	3
4) ventilate	4	4
5) lengthen	5	5
6) redden	6	6
7) mistaken	7	7
8) deaden	8	8
9) notify	9	9
10) magnify	10	10
11) purify	11	11
12) intensify	12	12
13) apologise	13	13
14) standardise	14	14
15) realise	15	15
16) moisturise	16	16
17) ability	17	17
18) stupidity	18	18
19) simplicity	19	19
20) necessity	20	20

EXTRA PRACTICE		
E1) quantify	E1	E1
E2) categorise	E2	E2

ate, en, ify, ise, ity

Put the flap over the last page and use the hints to work out the words.
Get _____ right to become a Spelling Superstar.

Hint hint	One last time...
1) What bees do to flowers.	1
2) Treat with medicine.	2
3) Fit with elastic.	3
4) Make air circulation better.	4
5) Make something longer.	5
6) Go red, or blush.	6
7) A case of _ _ _ _ _ _ _ _ identity.	7
8) Make a sound duller.	8
9) Point something out to someone.	9
10) Make something appear bigger.	10
11) Make something more pure.	11
12) Make more intense.	12
13) Say sorry.	13
14) Make everything the same.	14
15) The penny drops...	15
16) Make your skin nice and soft.	16
17) Being able to do something.	17
18) Being really thick.	18
19) Something being really simple.	19
20) Something that has to be done.	20

EXTRA PRACTICE

E1) Make the amount clear.	E1
E2) Put things into groups.	E2

Making f or fe words plural

Copy out the words once, cover with the flap and write them again.
Get _____ right to become a Spelling Superstar.

Read	Copy	Cover
1) loaf	1	1
2) loaves	2	2
3) thief	3	3
4) thieves	4	4
5) scarf	5	5
6) scarves	6	6
7) self	7	7
8) selves	8	8
9) cuff	9	9
10) cuffs	10	10
11) cliff	11	11
12) cliffs	12	12
13) bluff	13	13
14) bluffs	14	14
15) knife	15	15
16) knives	16	16
17) wife	17	17
18) wives	18	18
19) wolf	19	19
20) wolves	20	20

EXTRA PRACTICE		
E1) belief	E1	E1
E2) beliefs	E2	E2

Making f or fe words plural

Put the flap over the last page and use the hints to work out the words.
Get _____ right to become a Spelling Superstar.

Hint hint	One last time...
1) Bread comes in this form.	1 ....
2) More than one lump of bread.	2 ....
3) Someone who steals things.	3 ....
4) More than one stealing criminal.	4 ....
5) Keeps your neck warm.	5 ....
6) They warm lots of people's necks.	6 ....
7) Another word for 'me'.	7 ....
8) Plural of above word.	8 ....
9) Part of shirt near the wrist.	9 ....
10) Both shirt parts together.	10 ....
11) Rocky bit of land near the sea.	11 ....
12) More than one rocky bit of land.	12 ....
13) A trick to confuse someone.	13 ....
14) More than one trick.	14 ....
15) Sharp blade for cutting.	15 ....
16) More than one blade.	16 ....
17) The woman I married.	17 ....
18) The women we married.	18 ....
19) One of these:	19 ....
20) More than one number 19).	20 ....

EXTRA PRACTICE	
E1) Something I believe in.	E1 ....
E2) All the things I believe in.	E2 ....

ight, ious, ial, ough

Copy out the words once, cover with the flap and write them again.
Get _____ right to become a Spelling Superstar.

Read	Copy	Cover
1) light	1	1
2) fight	2	2
3) slight	3	3
4) bright	4	4
5) right	5	5
6) infectious	6	6
7) previous	7	7
8) tedious	8	8
9) glorious	9	9
10) curious	10	10
11) partial	11	11
12) official	12	12
13) racial	13	13
14) financial	14	14
15) social	15	15
16) bough	16	16
17) although	17	17
18) through	18	18
19) cough	19	19
20) rough	20	20

EXTRA PRACTICE		
E1) jovial	E1	E1
E2) serious	E2	E2

ight, ious, ial, ough

Put the flap over the last page and use the hints to work out the words.
Get _____ right to become a Spelling Superstar.

Hint hint	**One last time...**
1) Opposite of dark.	1 ....
2) Punch-up.	2 ....
3) Only a small amount.	3 ....
4) Shining a lot.	4 ....
5) Not left.	5 ....
6) His laughter was i _ f _ c _ i _ u _ .	6 ....
7) The one before.	7 ....
8) Really boring.	8 ....
9) Wonderful and sunny.	9 ....
10) Wondering why.	10 ....
11) Only part of something.	11 ....
12) Good and proper.	12 ....
13) To do with race.	13 ....
14) About money.	14 ....
15) About society.	15 ....
16) Branch of a tree.	16 ....
17) Even though.	17 ....
18) Right t _ r _ u _ h the middle.	18 ....
19) Clear your throat.	19 ....
20) Not smooth.	20 ....

EXTRA PRACTICE	
E1) Cheerful.	E1 ....
E2) Not cheerful.	E2 ....

ful, ly, ive, ist

Copy out the words once, cover with the flap and write them again.
Get _____ right to become a Spelling Superstar.

Read	Copy	Cover
1) hurtful	1	1
2) spiteful	2	2
3) painful	3	3
4) wonderful	4	4
5) beautiful	5	5
6) secretively	6	6
7) jokingly	7	7
8) speedily	8	8
9) wholly	9	9
10) curiously	10	10
11) explosive	11	11
12) corrosive	12	12
13) furtive	13	13
14) decorative	14	14
15) relative	15	15
16) extremist	16	16
17) violinist	17	17
18) artist	18	18
19) balloonist	19	19
20) specialist	20	20

EXTRA PRACTICE		
E1) mouthful	E1	E1
E2) pianist	E2	E2

ful, ly, ive, ist

Put the flap over the last page and use the hints to work out the words.
Get _____ right to become a Spelling Superstar.

Hint hint

1) Causing hurt.

2) Nasty on purpose.

3) Ouch!

4) Full of wonder.

5) He was be _ u _ i _ ul.

6) Done without anybody knowing.

7) Said in a funny way.

8) Really fast.

9) I w _ o _ l _ agree with you.

10) Doing something in a curious way.

11) Able to explode.

12) Able to corrode.

13) Secretive.

14) Looking pretty.

15) Someone you're related to.

16) A very extreme person.

17) This person:

18) A person who paints.

19) Someone riding in a hot-air balloon.

20) An expert.

One last time...

1 ....

2 ....

3 ....

4 ....

5 ....

6 ....

7 ....

8 ....

9 ....

10 ....

11 ....

12 ....

13 ....

14 ....

15 ....

16 ....

17 ....

18 ....

19 ....

20 ....

EXTRA PRACTICE

E1) Enough to fill your mouth.

E2) Piano player.

E1 ....

E2 ....

ible, able

Copy out the words once, cover with the flap and write them again.
Get _____ right to become a Spelling Superstar.

Read	Copy	Cover
1) horrible	1	1
2) responsible	2	2
3) edible	3	3
4) invincible	4	4
5) susceptible	5	5
6) terrible	6	6
7) possible	7	7
8) indestructible	8	8
9) reversible	9	9
10) compatible	10	10
11) miserable	11	11
12) adorable	12	12
13) disposable	13	13
14) breakable	14	14
15) reliable	15	15
16) valuable	16	16
17) probable	17	17
18) identifiable	18	18
19) forgivable	19	19
20) respectable	20	20

EXTRA PRACTICE		
E1) portable	E1	E1
E2) indubitable	E2	E2

ible, able

Put the flap over the last page and use the hints to work out the words.
Get _____ right to become a Spelling Superstar.

Hint hint	One last time...
1) Nasty and unpleasant.	1
2) Able to deal with responsibility.	2
3) Something you can eat.	3
4) Impossible to defeat.	4
5) Very s _ s _ e _ t _ ble to illness.	5
6) Full of terror.	6
7) Opposite of impossible.	7
8) Opposite of destructible.	8
9) Something you can reverse.	9
10) Able to get along with each other.	10
11) Full of misery.	11
12) Really lovely and sweet.	12
13) Stuff you can throw away.	13
14) Easy to break.	14
15) Something you can rely on.	15
16) Worth loads of money.	16
17) Likely to happen.	17
18) Possible to identify.	18
19) Opposite of unforgivable.	19
20) Something you can respect.	20

EXTRA PRACTICE

E1) Possible to carry around.	E1
E2) Something you can't doubt.	E2

tion, sion

Copy out the words once, cover with the flap and write them again.
Get _____ right to become a Spelling Superstar.

Read		Copy	Cover
1)	inflation	1	1
2)	vibration	2	2
3)	dictation	3	3
4)	education	4	4
5)	navigation	5	5
6)	creation	6	6
7)	temptation	7	7
8)	variation	8	8
9)	punctuation	9	9
10)	expectation	10	10
11)	decision	11	11
12)	division	12	12
13)	supervision	13	13
14)	explosion	14	14
15)	corrosion	15	15
16)	television	16	16
17)	collision	17	17
18)	extension	18	18
19)	transfusion	19	19
20)	confusion	20	20

EXTRA PRACTICE			
E1)	tension	E1	E1
E2)	portion	E2	E2

tion, sion

Put the flap over the last page and use the hints to work out the words.
Get _____ right to become a Spelling Superstar.

Hint hint	One last time...
1) Increase in the cost of things.	1 ....
2) Shaking up and down.	2 ....
3) Giving d _ cta _ i _ n.	3 ....
4) Learning stuff for years.	4 ....
5) The art of navigating.	5 ....
6) The moment something is created.	6 ....
7) Something that tempts you.	7 ....
8) A bit different from normal.	8 ....
9) Full stops and commas and stuff.	9 ....
10) What you reckon will happen.	10 ....
11) An important d _ c _ s _ o _ .	11 ....
12) A split.	12 ....
13) Only play under s _ p _ r _ i _ i _ n.	13 ....
14) A loud bang.	14 ....
15) The wearing away of things.	15 ....
16) One of these:	16 ....
17) Two things crashing into each other.	17 ....
18) An extra bit on a house.	18 ....
19) Blood t _ a _ s _ u _ i _ n.	19 ....
20) A complete muddle.	20 ....

EXTRA PRACTICE

E1) A worried atmosphere.	E1 ....
E2) One part of something.	E2 ....

Changing tense

Copy out the words once, cover with the flap and write them again.
Get _____ right to become a Spelling Superstar.

Read	Copy	Cover
1) blow	1	1
2) blew	2	2
3) drink	3	3
4) drank	4	4
5) feed	5	5
6) fed	6	6
7) creep	7	7
8) crept	8	8
9) sweep	9	9
10) swept	10	10
11) find	11	11
12) found	12	12
13) think	13	13
14) thought	14	14
15) tear	15	15
16) tore	16	16
17) write	17	17
18) wrote	18	18
19) slide	19	19
20) slid	20	20

EXTRA PRACTICE		
E1) enjoy	E1	E1
E2) enjoyed	E2	E2

Changing tense

Put the flap over the last page and use the hints to work out the words.
Get _____ right to become a Spelling Superstar.

Hint hint	One last time...
1) You know how to whistle?	1 ....
2) The past tense of 'blow'.	2 ....
3) Sip on your orange juice NOW.	3 ....
4) Yesterday you _ _ _ _ _ the juice.	4 ....
5) Giving food to something.	5 ....
6) No TV — I was really _ _ _ up.	6 ....
7) To walk very quietly.	7 ....
8) Past tense of 'creep'.	8 ....
9) Using a broom to clean up.	9 ....
10) I've _ _ _ _ _ up all the mess.	10 ....
11) Another word for 'discover'.	11 ....
12) Another word for 'discovered'.	12 ....
13) To wonder about something.	13 ....
14) To have wondered about it already.	14 ....
15) Rip something apart.	15 ....
16) To have ripped it apart yesterday.	16 ....
17) If you put pen to paper now.	17 ....
18) If you put pen to paper in 1999.	18 ....
19) Go down the slippery slope.	19 ....
20) Went down the slope.	20 ....

EXTRA PRACTICE

E1) I really like doing this.	E1 ....
E2) I really liked doing this.	E2 ....

Changing tense

Copy out the words once, cover with the flap and write them again.
Get _____ right to become a Spelling Superstar.

Read	Copy	Cover
1) eat	1	1
2) ate	2	2
3) go	3	3
4) went	4	4
5) are	5	5
6) were	6	6
7) does	7	7
8) did	8	8
9) teach	9	9
10) taught	10	10
11) catch	11	11
12) caught	12	12
13) send	13	13
14) sent	14	14
15) sit	15	15
16) sat	16	16
17) hear	17	17
18) heard	18	18
19) can	19	19
20) could	20	20

EXTRA PRACTICE		
E1) annoy	E1	E1
E2) annoyed	E2	E2

Changing tense

Put the flap over the last page and use the hints to work out the words.
Get _____ right to become a Spelling Superstar.

Hint hint	One last time...
1) Stuff your face.	1 ....
2) Stuffed your face.	2 ....
3) Head off somewhere.	3 ....
4) The past tense of 'go'.	4 ....
5) We _ _ _ going on a long break.	5 ....
6) Last week we _ _ _ _ on holiday.	6 ....
7) What _ _ _ _ it all mean?	7 ....
8) The past tense of 'does'.	8 ....
9) Help people learn stuff.	9 ....
10) To have helped people learn stuff.	10 ....
11) Snatch the ball out of the air.	11 ....
12) Yesterday, I c _ u _ h _ chickenpox.	12 ....
13) To put a letter in the post.	13 ....
14) To have already put it in the post.	14 ....
15) Rest in a chair.	15 ....
16) To have rested in a chair last night.	16 ....
17) You do it with your ears.	17 ....
18) Have you _ _ _ _ _ the news?	18 ....
19) Other way of saying 'able to'.	19 ....
20) Other way of saying 'was able to'.	20 ....

EXTRA PRACTICE	
E1) Get on my nerves.	E1 ....
E2) Got on my nerves.	E2 ....

35

Different sounds spelt the same

Copy out the words once, cover with the flap and write them again.
Get _____ right to become a Spelling Superstar.

Read	Copy	Cover
1) tough	1	1
2) enough	2	2
3) trough	3	3
4) cough	4	4
5) plough	5	5
6) rough	6	6
7) through	7	7
8) thought	8	8
9) bear	9	9
10) hear	10	10
11) learn	11	11
12) earn	12	12
13) wear	13	13
14) dreary	14	14
15) fear	15	15
16) light	16	16
17) weight	17	17
18) sight	18	18
19) freight	19	19
20) bright	20	20

EXTRA PRACTICE		
E1) hearth	E1	E1
E2) thorough	E2	E2

Spelling Book 2 — Tough Words

© CGP 2002

Different sounds spelt the same

Put the flap over the last page and use the hints to work out the words.
Get _____ right to become a Spelling Superstar.

Hint hint	One last time...
1) Opposite of tender.	1 ....
2) "That's it — I've had _ _ _ _ _ _."	2 ....
3) What pigs eat out of.	3 ....
4) You can get one when you're ill.	4 ....
5) Farm machine.	5 ....
6) Opposite of smooth.	6 ....
7) Go _ _ _ _ _ _ _ a tunnel.	7 ....
8) An idea.	8 ....
9) Big hairy animal. Grizzly.	9 ....
10) Listen.	10 ....
11) What you do at school.	11 ....
12) Make money.	12 ....
13) You _ _ _ _ clothes.	13 ....
14) Boring and dull.	14 ....
15) Fright.	15 ....
16) Opposite of dark.	16 ....
17) A heavy thing.	17 ....
18) Seeing.	18 ....
19) Heavy stuff carried by trains.	19 ....
20) Opposite of dull.	20 ....

EXTRA PRACTICE

E1) The floor in front of the fire.	E1 ....
E2) Doing a job carefully.	E2 ....

Different sounds spelt the same

Copy out the words once, cover with the flap and write them again.
Get _____ right to become a Spelling Superstar.

Read	Copy	Cover
1) out	1	1
2) shout	2	2
3) hour	3	3
4) pour	4	4
5) four	5	5
6) mourn	6	6
7) route	7	7
8) journey	8	8
9) aunt	9	9
10) haunt	10	10
11) sausage	11	11
12) sauce	12	12
13) because	13	13
14) trauma	14	14
15) practice	15	15
16) notice	16	16
17) spice	17	17
18) police	18	18
19) twice	19	19
20) Alice	20	20

EXTRA PRACTICE		
E1) apprentice	E1	E1
E2) autumn	E2	E2

Different sounds spelt the same

Put the flap over the last page and use the hints to work out the words.
Get _____ right to become a Spelling Superstar.

Hint hint	One last time...
1) Opposite of in.	1 ....
2) Speak loudly.	2 ....
3) 60 minutes.	3 ....
4) Tip out liquid.	4 ....
5) One more than three.	5 ....
6) Feel sad about someone who died.	6 ....
7) The path you take to go somewhere.	7 ....
8) A long trip.	8 ....
9) Your uncle's wife.	9 ....
10) Ghosts do this.	10 ....
11) One of these:	11 ....
12) Ketchup is one.	12 ....
13) Explains why.	13 ....
14) Emotional shock.	14 ....
15) Repeating things to get better.	15 ....
16) A sign giving information.	16 ....
17) Like a herb, but hotter.	17 ....
18) They can arrest people.	18 ....
19) Once, _ _ _ _ _, three times	19 ....
20) A girl's name beginning with A.	20 ....

EXTRA PRACTICE

E1) Someone learning a job.	E1 ....
E2) Season before winter.	E2 ....

Spelling Book 2 — Tough Words

Sticking words together

Copy out the words once, cover with the flap and write them again.
Get _____ right to become a Spelling Superstar.

Read	Copy	Cover
1) inwards	1	1
2) sunshine	2	2
3) someone	3	3
4) landlord	4	4
5) bedroom	5	5
6) cloakroom	6	6
7) teapot	7	7
8) popcorn	8	8
9) inside	9	9
10) goodnight	10	10
11) dustbin	11	11
12) handbag	12	12
13) starboard	13	13
14) blackbird	14	14
15) database	15	15
16) everyone	16	16
17) somewhere	17	17
18) snowboard	18	18
19) outside	19	19
20) grasshopper	20	20

EXTRA PRACTICE		
E1) grandmother	E1	E1
E2) cupboard	E2	E2

Sticking words together

Put the flap over the last page and use the hints to work out the words.
Get _____ right to become a Spelling Superstar.

Hint hint	One last time...
1) Opposite of outwards.	1 ....
2) A bright day full of:	2 ....
3) Opposite of no one.	3 ....
4) People pay him rent.	4 ....
5) The room you sleep in.	5 ....
6) The room to put coats in.	6 ....
7) You brew tea in it.	7 ....
8) What you eat at the cinema.	8 ....
9) Opposite of outside.	9 ....
10) What you say before bed.	10 ....
11) Where you put the rubbish.	11 ....
12) Ladies carry things in them.	12 ....
13) The right-hand side of a boat.	13 ....
14) A bird the colour of night.	14 ....
15) A computer program with numbers.	15 ....
16) All the people.	16 ....
17) Opposite of nowhere.	17 ....
18) Bigger than a ski.	18 ....
19) Opposite of inside.	19 ....
20) Like a cricket.	20 ....

EXTRA PRACTICE

E1) Married to your grandfather.	E1 ....
E2) Where you put away plates.	E2 ....

© CGP 2002

Spelling Book 2 — Tough Words

Homophones are words that sound the same, but have different meanings.

Homophones

Copy out the words once, cover with the flap and write them again.
Get _____ right to become a Spelling Superstar.

Read	Copy	Cover
1) right	1	1
2) write	2	2
3) hole	3	3
4) whole	4	4
5) are	5	5
6) our	6	6
7) there	7	7
8) their	8	8
9) you	9	9
10) yew	10	10
11) inn	11	11
12) in	12	12
13) heard	13	13
14) herd	14	14
15) place	15	15
16) plaice	16	16
17) be	17	17
18) bee	18	18
19) might	19	19
20) mite	20	20

EXTRA PRACTICE		
E1) through	E1	E1
E2) threw	E2	E2

Homophones

Put the flap over the last page and use the hints to work out the words.
Get _____ right to become a Spelling Superstar.

Hint hint

1) Opposite of left.

2) You use a pen to _ _ _ _ _.

3) A gap in something. ⬜

4) Everything.

5) They _ _ _ everywhere.

6) They belong to us. They're _ _ _ toys.

7) She's over _ _ _ _ _.

8) It belongs to them; it's _ _ _ _ _ house.

9) Not me but _ _ _.

10) Type of tree.

11) A pub.

12) Opposite of out.

13) Listened.

14) A group of cows.

15) A bit of ground.

16) Type of flat fish.

17) Shakespeare: "to _ _ or not to _ _"

18) Like a wasp, but fatter.

19) Means the same as maybe.

20) Small bug.

One last time...

1 ....
2 ....
3 ....
4 ....
5 ....
6 ....
7 ....
8 ....
9 ....
10 ....
11 ....
12 ....
13 ....
14 ....
15 ....
16 ....
17 ....
18 ....
19 ....
20 ....

EXTRA PRACTICE

E1) Push the pin _ _ _ _ _ _ _ the cloth.

E2) I just _ _ _ _ _ a ball.

E1 ....
E2 ....

Smallness words

Copy out the words once, cover with the flap and write them again.
Get _____ right to become a Spelling Superstar.

Read	Copy	Cover
1) miniskirt	1	1
2) minibus	2	2
3) minuscule	3	3
4) minimum	4	4
5) miniature	5	5
6) brunette	6	6
7) cigarette	7	7
8) sapling	8	8
9) duckling	9	9
10) gosling	10	10
11) dumpling	11	11
12) microchip	12	12
13) microphone	13	13
14) microscope	14	14
15) itsy-bitsy	15	15
16) small	16	16
17) tiny	17	17
18) less	18	18
19) junior	19	19
20) baby	20	20

EXTRA PRACTICE		
E1) minicomputer	E1	E1
E2) majorette	E2	E2